SAL
BALLADS

SALT-WATER BALLADS

John Masefield

Introduction by Philip W. Errington, Department of
Printed Books and Manuscripts, Sotheby's, and Visiting
Research Fellow, University of London

THE CYDER PRESS
Cheltenham, England

Acknowledgements

The Cyder Press is indebted to The Society of Authors, as the literary representative of the Estate of John Masefield, for permission to reprint the first edition of *Salt-Water Ballads* (London: Grant Richards, 1902) in its original form.

This edition first published by The Cyder Press, 2002

ISBN 1 86174 124 3

Published and produced by the University of Gloucestershire, 2002

INTRODUCTION

John Betjeman claimed that John Masefield's 'Sea-Fever' would be 'remembered as long as the language lasts'.[1] The famous poem first appeared, in volume publication, in *Salt-Water Ballads*. This was also John Masefield's first book, and merely the inclusion of 'Sea-Fever' claims a distinguished position for the volume in the annals of English literature. It is not this fact alone, however, that demands attention. The volume contains over fifty poems written with a freshness and authenticity of diction that Masefield considered 'something new said newly'.[2]

Masefield was born in 1878, and after the death of his parents, was educated aboard the training-ship H.M.S. *Conway*. His marine schooling instructed him for the sea but also, crucially, introduced him to marine history, mythology and yarns. Gaining the position of a senior petty officer, Masefield left the ship in 1894 and was apprenticed to a four-masted barque sailing from Cardiff to Iquique in Chile via Cape Horn. The new apprentice was violently ill, and upon arrival, sunstroke combined with a nervous breakdown. He was classified as a Distressed British Seaman, and after time in hospital, returned to England. Arrangements were made for the young man to join another vessel in New York. Masefield had other plans, however, and upon arrival in America he deserted ship. Following years of homeless vagrancy, bar and factory work in the United States, Masefield returned to England in 1899. He had vowed he was going to 'become a writer come what might'.[3] Whilst working as a bank clerk, he began to get his poems published in periodicals and drew encouragement from W.B. Yeats. With publication of *Salt-Water Ballads* by Grant Richards, Masefield was to embark on a publishing career that would continue for over six decades.

Grant Richards held a distinguished – although precarious – position within the publishing world at the beginning of the twentieth century. His list included G.K. Chesterton, A.E. Housman and George Bernard Shaw, and he was later to support James Joyce, but his financial security was never safe. He also appears to have a less than reliable memory. In his autobiographical *Author Hunting* (Hamish Hamilton, 1934), Richards notes that he made the initial suggestion to publish a volume of Masefield's poetry after reading 'The West Wind' in *The Nation*, but he is presumably referring to 'There's a Wind A-Blowing' in *The Speaker*, published on 28 June 1902. At the time of publication, approximately half of the poems in *Salt-Water Ballads* had previously appeared in periodicals. *The Speaker*, it seems, was especially willing to publish Masefield's work.

The Speaker was a leading Liberal journal (founded in 1818). We might therefore ask whether there was a political agenda behind the early Masefield. His political stance changed over his lengthy career and Masefield became increasingly apolitical. However, his earliest verse – and the poem that introduces *Salt-Water Ballads* in particular – suggests a voice of some political fervour. This is an angry young man trying to make a forthright statement. Later, of course, the Poet Laureate may have been embarrassed that his first volume opens with a rejection '… of the princes and prelates with periwigged charioteers/Riding triumphantly laurelled to lap the fat of the years …'. But it is an arresting and emphatic statement clearly demonstrating that Masefield will side with the under-dog: the typical Masefield hero, whose triumph is defeat, is first manifest here.

The earliest extant letters of Masefield to Richards suggest that the unknown author relied on his publisher for advice. The final months before publication saw much activity. An early discussion concerned the title. Apparently that on which Masefield had 'set his heart' had 'been already collared viz *Spunyarn*'.[4] Ever helpful, the author then provided nine alternatives: *Sea Drift, Waif o' the Sea, Spindrift, Blue-Water Lyrics, Ballads of Wind and Tide, Marks and Deeps, Bag o' Wrinkle, Halliard Chanties* and *Hank o' Yarn*. Richards, it appears, suggested *Salt-Water Ballads*, and was later to regret the comparison this invited with Rudyard Kipling's *Barrack-Room Ballads*. Both the title and the style of binding were to be similar. Masefield agreed with Richards's suggestion early in September 1902, noting it 'seems to me to be a good title'.[5] Discussion could now centre on the contents of the volume.

Richards' reader (possibly E.V. Lucas) had early reservations, and the publisher notified Masefield of this reception. The author responded with characteristic modesty and self-deprecation: 'I quite agree with your reader that some of the stuff ought to be omitted ... . As I am not a good critic will you please ask your reader to let me know which he especially objects to so that I can form a saner estimate of my shortcomings?'.[6] One apparent short-coming was Masefield's diction, and specifically, use of the word 'bloody'.

Masefield was later to create a sensation with his use of colloquial diction in *The Everlasting Mercy* (the 'offensive' word was blanked out of *The English Review*'s publication of this poem in October 1911). Richards was also to encounter 'bloody' in Joyce's *Dubliners*, and this early debate between Masefield and Richards is therefore of interest. In a letter dated 7 September 1902, Masefield, with typical fun, suggests that prudery is misplaced considering what he *could* have written. Suddenly, when he contemplates that the volume's success may be threatened, he makes it clear that Richards is firmly in control:

> I have been thinking over the word 'bloody' and have decided to use it sparingly, feeling that it is not a very popular adjective at sea; marine taste preferring a coarser and more expressive word, an equivalent to tell the truth, for 'copulating'. I want to ask you, also, if, in your opinion, a freedom of the kind would militate in any way against the book's chances. Personally I don't think it would but I should like to be guided by your experience in these matters ... .[7]

Later in the same month, Masefield was noting that Byron uses the word, 'and with Smollett and Marryat it becomes a recognised and accepted intensive'.[8] The word was eventually printed with a note in the glossary stating it was 'an intensive derived from the substantive "blood" ...'. Masefield is – in many ways – often a humorous writer, and his sense of fun is apparent here.

Salt-Water Ballads was intended to be difficult and idiomatic, if not shocking. Writing to his family, the author noted that he thought the book

> deserves the recognition of a maritime people ... . There is such a deal of cant, shoddy, humbug, drivel etc. going around, it is quite likely the book'll get killed before Christmas, but I feel that, in any case, I've said a straight word sure to be recognized as such by some few ... .[9]

The provision of a glossary to the volume (appreciated by at least two contemporary reviewers) suggests Masefield's own doubts, and in sending the text of the glossary to Richards during the middle of September 1902, Masefield notes: 'I'm afraid that these sea-terms will prove great stumbling blocks to most'.[10] The experiment of *Salt-Water Ballads* was to be cautiously re-visited by Masefield in his career, but it may be significant that his second volume, *Ballads*, published the following year, was far more lyrical and pastoral in diction and subject.

A lengthy review in *Academy and Literature* stated: 'these poems have the brine in their timbers and are green with weed; the wind shrills in them, they are hearty and strong with the tarry vocabulary of sailor-folk – not clipped and essenced for shore-use and the pretty lips of pretty ladies...'. Despite finding the volume 'remarkable', the reviewer noted, however, that Kipling, Housman and Yeats were obvious influences. *The Outlook* published a short three sentence review, declaring the volume 'suitably breezy and briny'. The *Times Literary Supplement* made reference to 'Mr. Masefield's gift', and noted 'a certain power he has of handling with effect an unusual or varied metre'.

The volume is interesting for Masefield's early use and manipulation of metre and rhyme. Many of the poems are difficult to scan, and Masefield frequently uses clusters of monosyllabic words to slow his readers and vary pace. There are, admittedly, some trite and common-place rhymes, but also some effective treatments. The *aaab* scheme of 'Cardigan Bay', for example, brings a sudden force to the last word of the last stanza. This poem also demonstrates Masefield's use of contrasts: the wild and dramatic action above water (featuring some brisk present participles) contrasts suddenly with the stillness below water. The drive and energy of the first two stanzas have diverted attention away from the 'hidden rocks', and the calm tranquility of the sailors' graves jars the reader abruptly. Throughout the collection, there is a lack of sentimentality. Masefield focuses on the harshness of life, pervaded by a strong presence of death. The poems are personal, but not autobiographical.

When, in 1923, an American edition reprinted *Salt-Water Ballads* within *Salt Water Ballads and Poems*, Masefield provided an introduction in which he claims an historical context for the subject of the book.[11] He draws particular attention, however, to language and stresses the harshness of sea life:

> I began to write these verses at a very early age .... . They are all a young man's work, and most of them deal with the life of the sailor and the alongshore man. The sailor of those far-away days is now almost extinct. He was unlike any kind of sailor to be met with nowadays. At that time the bulk of the carrying trade in the world was done in sailing ships, making long voyages, and remaining sometimes two or three years from any home port. The sailors of those ships, from living long at sea, were a race apart. They talked almost a language of their own. They lived the hardest life known to men; in frequent danger, constant exposure, continual overwork, and occasional ill-treatment. Shut off, as they were, from the shore for many months at a time, they had to make their own amusements, or do without them. It was said that they made their money like horses, and spent it like asses. But they never spent any money. It was always taken from them long before they had the chance to spend it. I have known sailors come ashore from a two years' voyage with seventy or eighty pounds in their pockets. They would retain their money and their consciousness for perhaps half an hour after being paid off, and would recover consciousness to find themselves on board some outward-bound ship which they had never seen, condemned to serve for another two years before the process could be repeated. It was said of such sailors that you

could not kill them with axes: that their hairs were rope-yarn, their fingers fish-hooks, and their blood 'like good Stockhollum tar'. They were a race apart, like the cowboy. A strong need brought them into being. For a few years the cowboy could compete with the railway in driving vast herds of cattle from Texas into Montana; and for a few years the iron cargo-carrying sailing ships could compete with the steamer over certain routes with certain freights. In both ways of life all that was wild-blooded and adventurous found an opportunity. Both ways of life passed away, leaving no trace save the memories of lawlessness and a few wild songs. In 'Salt-Water Ballads' I tried to set down a hint or two of that old way of life, by which our bread was carried and paid for nearly forty years ago.

Despite general enthusiasm in 1902 (Richards received the first application to set some verses to music less than a fortnight after publication[12]), Masefield's biographer, Constance Babington Smith, is incorrect in stating 'within about six months' the edition had 'completely sold out'.[13] When Richards' business went bankrupt in 1904, stock was sold to Alexander Moring of the De La More press. In 1906, there appear to have been 53 unbound and 11 bound copies.[14] Masefield wrote in 1913 that, '... about ten years ago, I published an unsuccessful book called *Salt Water Ballads* of which very few were sold before the publisher went bankrupt ...', but the author's account is undoubtedly pessimistic about sales.[15]

Once the rights to the book had been re-acquired (probably in 1906), it is perhaps significant that Masefield would not agree to republication of the title until 1913. The writer was developing his literary voice during the period, culminating in publication of *The Everlasting Mercy* in 1911, and it seems that Masefield thought the reappearance of his first volume was undesirable. When eventually republished (by Elkin Mathews), the new edition had been slightly revised (some abbreviated words were lengthened, an occasional word was changed, and the dedications were removed). By 1913, however, Masefield was gaining in popularity, and the revised text sold extremely well (by 1922, new impressions consisted of at least 2000 copies, and by 1924, the publishers had brought out a ninth impression). An application to publish a Braille version was received in 1930, and there was even a German translation published in 1951. In 1923, the volume was included in *Collected Poems* which, between then and 1930, was to sell more than 100,000 copies.[16] In America, *Salt-Water Ballads* was first published in 1913 and formed the basis of a 1916 volume entitled *Salt-Water Poems and Ballads*. The latter volume, with illustrations by Charles Pears, was reprinted many, many times. 1915 saw the publication of John Ireland's musical setting of 'Sea Fever', and the status of *Salt-Water Ballads* was assured. The first edition of 1902 was never reprinted, however, and the original text presenting Masefield's earliest work has been unknown apart from the 500 copies of the first printing.

It is therefore a great pleasure to introduce a facsimile of the first edition in this, the centenary year of its first publication. The copy from which this reproduction has been made is in the Library of The John Masefield Society.

Philip W. Errington
London

NOTES

1   John Betjeman, 'Introduction' to John Masefield, *Selected Poems*, Heinemann, 1978, p.vii.

2.   John Masefield, letter to Harry Ross, 1 December 1902 (Private Collection. See Constance Babington Smith, *John Masefield – A Life*, Oxford, 1978, p.72).

3.   John Masefield, Autobiographical Notes sent to Elizabeth Robins, [1910?] (New York Public Library, Berg Collection. See Constance Babington Smith, *John Masefield – A Life, op cit*, p.32).

4.   John Masefield, letter to Grant Richards, 29 August 1902 (New York Public Library, Berg Collection).

5.   John Masefield, letter to Grant Richards, 3 September 1902 (New York Public Library, Berg Collection).

6.   John Masefield, letter to Grant Richards, 29 August 1902 (New York Public Library, Berg Collection).

7.   John Masefield, letter to Grant Richards, 7 September 1902 (Harvard University, Houghton Library; *61M-93).

8. John Masefield, letter to Grant Richards, 19 September 1902 (New York Public Library, Berg Collection).

9. John Masefield, letter to Harry Ross, 1 December 1902 (Private Collection. See Constance Babington Smith, *John Masefield – A Life, op cit,* p.72)

10. John Masefield, letter to Grant Richards, 17 September 1902 (New York Public Library, Berg Collection).

11. See John Masefield, *Salt Water Ballads and Poems*, Macmillan, 1923 (issued as part of Macmillan's 'Leather Pocket Edition'). This volume should not be confused with *Salt-Water Poems and Ballads.*

12. Richards wrote to Masefield on 22 November 1902, enclosing a letter from Francis Allitsen. Richards' letter is acknowledged in Masefield's reply, dated 24 November 1902 (see New York Public Library, Berg Collection).

13. Constance Babington Smith, *John Masefield – A Life, op cit,* p.73

14. Masefield wrote to the De La More Press in January 1906, and this letter has been annotated by the recipient with sales information. See John Masefield, [letter to Alexander Moring?], [January 1906?] (New York Public Library, Berg Collection).

15. John Masefield, letter to Constance Belliss, 1 April 1913 (Harvard University, Houghton Library; *68M-108).

16. As reported by William Buchan (see William Buchan, 'Introduction' to John Masefield, *Letters to Reyna*, Buchan and Enright, 1983, p.26).

SALT-WATER BALLADS

SALT-WATER
BALLADS

BY

JOHN MASEFIELD

GRANT RICHARDS
48 LEICESTER SQUARE
LONDON
1902

Edinburgh: Printed by T. and A. CONSTABLE

TO

C. DE LA CHEROIS CROMMELIN

A. HANFORD-FLOOD

AND

H. M. HEANE

I thank the Editors of the *Broad-Sheet, Outlook, Pall Mall Magazine, Speaker,* and *Tatler,* for permission to include in this volume a number of ballads which originally appeared in those papers. JOHN MASEFIELD.

CONTENTS

CONTENTS

'The mariners are a pleasant people, but little
like those in the towns, and they can speak no other
language than that used in ships.'

The Licentiate Vidriera.

A CONSECRATION

Not of the princes and prelates with periwigged charioteers
Riding triumphantly laurelled to lap the fat of the years,—
Rather the scorned—the rejected—the men hemmed in with the spears;

The men of the tattered battalion which fights till it dies,
Dazed with the dust of the battle, the din and the cries,
The men with the broken heads and the blood running into their eyes.

Not the be-medalled Commander, beloved of the throne,
Riding cock-horse to parade when the bugles are blown,
But the lads who carried the koppie and cannot be known.

A

Not the ruler for me, but the ranker, the tramp of the road,
The slave with the sack on his shoulders pricked on with
*   the goad,*
The man with too weighty a burden, too weary a load.

The sailor, the stoker of steamers, the man with the
*   clout,*
The chantyman bent at the halliards putting a tune to
*   the shout,*
The drowsy man at the wheel and the tired look-out.

Others may sing of the wine and the wealth and the
*   mirth,*
The portly presence of potentates goodly in girth ;—
Mine be the dirt and the dross, the dust and scum of
*   the earth !*

THEIRS be the music, the colour, the glory, the gold ;
Mine be a handful of ashes, a mouthful of mould.
Of the maimed, of the halt and the blind in the rain
*   and the cold—*

Of these shall my songs be fashioned, my tales be told.

AMEN.

THE YARN OF THE 'LOCH ACHRAY'

THE 'Loch Achray' was a clipper tall
With seven-and-twenty hands in all.
Twenty to hand and reef and haul,
A skipper to sail and mates to bawl
'Tally on to the tackle-fall,
Heave now 'n' start her, heave 'n' pawl!'
       Hear the yarn of a sailor,
       An old yarn learned at sea.

Her crew was shipped and they said 'Farewell,
So-long, my Tottie, my lovely gell;
We sail to-day if we fetch to hell,
It's time we tackled the wheel a spell.'
       Hear the yarn of a sailor,
       An old yarn learned at sea.

The dockside loafers talked on the quay
The day that she towed down to sea:

'Lord, what a handsome ship she be!
Cheer her, sonny boys, three times three!'
And the dockside loafers gave her a shout
As the red-funnelled tug-boat towed her out;
They gave her a cheer as the custom is,
And the crew yelled 'Take our loves to Liz—
Three cheers, bullies, for old Pier Head
'N' the bloody stay-at-homes!' they said.
      Hear the yarn of a sailor,
      An old yarn learned at sea.

In the grey of the coming on of night
She dropped the tug at the Tuskar Light,
'N' the topsails went to the topmast head
To a chorus that fairly awoke the dead.
She trimmed her yards and slanted South
With her royals set and a bone in her mouth.
      Hear the yarn of a sailor,
      An old yarn learned at sea.

She crossed the Line and all went well,
They ate, they slept, and they struck the bell

And I give you a gospel truth when I state
The crowd didn't find any fault with the Mate,
But one night off of the River Plate.
  Hear the yarn of a sailor,
  An old yarn learned at sea.

It freshened up till it blew like thunder
And burrowed her deep, lee-scuppers under.
The old man said, 'I mean to hang on
Till her canvas busts or her sticks are gone'—
Which the blushing looney did, till at last
Overboard went her mizzen-mast.
  Hear the yarn of a sailor,
  An old yarn learned at sea.

Then a fierce squall struck the 'Loch Achray'
And bowed her down to her water-way;
Her main-shrouds gave and her forestay,
And a green sea carried her wheel away;
Ere the watch below had time to dress
She was cluttered up in a blushing mess.
  Hear the yarn of a sailor,
  An old yarn learned at sea.

She couldn't lay-to nor yet pay-off,
And she got swept clean in the bloody trough ;
Her masts were gone, and afore you knowed
She filled by the head and down she goed.
Her crew made seven-and-twenty dishes
For the big jack-sharks and the little fishes,
And over their bones the water swishes.
      Hear the yarn of a sailor,
      An old yarn learned at sea.

The wives and girls they watch in the rain
For a ship as won't come home again.
' I reckon it's them head-winds,' they say,
' She'll be home to-morrow, if not to-day.
I'll just nip home 'n' I'll air the sheets
'N' buy the fixins 'n' cook the meats
As my man likes 'n' as my man eats.'

So home they goes by the windy streets,
Thinking their men are homeward bound
With anchors *hungry* for English ground,
And the bloody fun of it is, *they're drowned !*
      Hear the yarn of a sailor,
      An old yarn learned at sea.

SING A SONG O' SHIPWRECK

HE lolled on a bollard, a sun-burned son of the sea,
With ear-rings of brass and a jumper of dungaree,
' 'N' many a queer lash-up have I seen,' says he.

' But the toughest hooray o' the racket,' he says,
    ' I 'll be sworn,
'N' the roughest traverse I worked since the day I
    was born,
Was a packet o' Sailor's Delight as I scoffed in the
    seas o' the Horn.

' All day long in the calm she had rolled to the
    swell,
Rolling through fifty degrees till she clattered her
    bell;
'N' then came snow, 'n' a squall, 'n' a wind was
    colder 'n hell.

' It blew like the Bull of Barney, a beast of a breeze,
'N' over the rail come the cold green lollopin' seas,
'N' she went ashore at the dawn on the Ramirez.

' She was settlin' down by the stern when I got to
      the deck,
Her waist was a smother o' sea as was up to your
      neck,
'N' her masts were gone, 'n' her rails, 'n' she was a
      wreck.

' We rigged up a tackle, a purchase, a sort of a shift,
To hoist the boats off o' the deck-house and get
      them adrift,
When her stern gives a sickenin' settle, her bows
      give a lift,

' 'N' smash comes a crash of green water as sets me
      afloat
With freezing fingers clutching the keel of a boat—
The bottom-up whaler—'n' that was the juice of
      a note.

'Well, I clambers acrost o' the keel 'n' I gets me
    secured,
When I sees a face in the white o' the smother to
    looard,
So I gives 'im a 'and, 'n' be shot if it wasn't the
    stooard !

'So he climbs up forrard o' me, 'n' "thanky," a' says,
'N' we sits 'n' shivers 'n' freeze to the bone wi' the
    sprays,
'N' *I* sings "Abel Brown," 'n' the stooard he prays.

'Wi' never a dollop to sup nor a morsel to bite,
The lips of us blue with the cold 'n' the heads of
    us light,
Adrift in a Cape Horn sea for a day 'n' a night.

''N' then the stooard goes dotty 'n' puts a tune to
    his lip,
'N' moans about Love like a dern old hen wi' the
    pip—
(I sets no store upon stooards—they ain't no use
    on a ship).

‘’N’ “mother,” the looney cackles, “come 'n' put
  Willy to bed ! ”
So I says “ Dry up, or I 'll fetch you a crack o' the
  head ” ;
“ The kettle's a-bilin',” he answers, “ 'n' I 'll go
  butter the bread.”

‘’N’ he falls to singin' some slush about clinkin' a
  can,
’N’ at last he dies, so he does, 'n' I tells you, Jan,
I was glad when he did, for he weren't no fun for a
  man.

‘ So he falls forrard, he does, 'n' he closes his eye,
’N’ quiet he lays 'n' quiet I leaves him lie,
’N’ I was alone with his corp, 'n' the cold green
  sea and the sky.

‘’N’ then I dithers, I guess, for the next as I knew
Was the voice of a mate as was sayin' to one of the
  crew,
“ Easy, my son, wi' the brandy, be shot if he ain't
  comin'-to ! ” ’

BURIAL PARTY

' He 's deader 'n nails,' the fo'c's'le said, ' 'n' gone to
    his long sleep ' ;
' 'N' about his corp,' said Tom to Dan, ' d 'ye think
    his corp 'll keep
Till the day 's done, 'n' the work 's through, 'n' the
    ebb 's upon the neap ? '

' He 's deader 'n nails,' said Dan to Tom, ' 'n' I wish
    his sperrit j'y ;
He spat straight 'n' he steered true, but listen to
    me, say I,
Take 'n' cover 'n' bury him now, 'n' I 'll take 'n'
    tell you why.

' It 's a rummy rig of a guffy's yarn, 'n' the juice of
    a rummy note,
But if you buries a corp at night, it takes 'n' keeps
    afloat,

For its bloody soul's afraid o' the dark 'n' sticks
    within the throat.

''N' all the night till the grey o' the dawn the dead
    'un has to swim
With a blue 'n' beastly Will o' the Wisp a-burnin'
    over him,
With a herring, maybe, a-scoffin' a toe or a shark
    a-chewin' a limb.

''N' all the night the shiverin' corp it has to swim
    the sea,
With its shudderin' soul inside the throat (where a
    soul's no right to be),
Till the sky's grey 'n' the dawn's clear, 'n' then
    the sperrit's free.

'Now Joe was a man was right as rain. I'm sort of
    sore for Joe,
'N' if we bury him durin' the day, his soul can take
    'n' go;
So we'll dump his corp when the bell strikes 'n' we
    can get below.

' I 'd fairly hate for him to swim in a blue 'n' beastly
    light,
With his shudderin' soul inside of him a-feelin' the
    fishes bite,
So over he goes at noon, say I, 'n' he shall sleep to-
    night.'

BILL

He lay dead on the cluttered deck and stared at
    the cold skies,
With never a friend to mourn for him nor a hand
    to close his eyes :
'Bill, he's dead,' was all they said ; 'he's dead, 'n'
    there he lies.'

The mate came forrard at seven bells and spat
    across the rail :
'Just lash him up wi' some holystone in a clout o'
    rotten sail,
'N', rot ye, get a gait on ye, ye're slower'n a
    bloody snail!'

When the rising moon was a copper disc and the
    sea was a strip of steel,
We dumped him down to the swaying weeds ten
    fathom beneath the keel.
'It's rough about Bill,' the fo'c's'le said, 'we'll
    have to stand his wheel.'

FEVER SHIP

THERE 'LL be no weepin' gells ashore when *our* ship
    sails,
Nor no crews cheerin' us, standin' at the rails,
'N' no Blue Peter a-foul the royal stay,
For we 've the Yellow Fever—Harry died to-day.—
    It 's cruel when a fo'c's'le gets the fever!

'N' Dick has got the fever-shakes, 'n' look what I
    was told
(I went to get a sack for him to keep him from the
    cold) :
' Sir, can I have a sack ? ' I says, ' for Dick 'e 's fit
    to die.'
' Oh, sack be shot ! ' the skipper says, ' jest let the
    rotter lie ! '—
    It 's cruel when a fo'c's'le gets the fever!

It's a cruel port is Santos, and a hungry land,
With rows o' graves already dug in yonder strip of
    sand,
'N' Dick is hollerin' up the hatch, 'e says 'e's goin'
    blue,
His pore teeth are chattering, 'n' what's a man to
    do ?—
    It's cruel when a fo'c's'le gets the fever !

FEVER-CHILLS

He tottered out of the alleyway with cheeks the
    colour of paste,
And shivered a spell and mopped his brow with
    a clout of cotton waste :
' I 've a lick of fever-chills,' he said, ' 'n' my inside
    it 's green,
But I 'd be as right as rain,' he said, ' if I had some
    quinine,—
    But there ain't no quinine for us poor sailor-men.

' But them there passengers,' he said, ' if they gets
    fever-chills,
There 's brimmin' buckets o' quinine for them, 'n'
    bulgin' crates o' pills,
'N' a doctor with Latin 'n' drugs 'n' all—enough
    to sink a town,
'N' they lies quiet in their blushin' bunks 'n' mops
    their gruel down,—

B

But there ain't none o' them fine ways for us
poor sailor-men.

' But the Chief comes forrard 'n' he says, says he,
" I gives you a straight tip :
Come none o' your Cape Horn fever lays aboard o'
     this yer ship.
On wi' your rags o' duds, my son, 'n' aft, 'n' down
     the hole :
The best cure known for fever-chills is shovelling
     bloody coal."
  It's *hard,* my son, that's what it is, for us poor
     sailor-men.'

ONE OF THE BO'SUN'S YARNS

LOAFIN' around in Sailor Town, a-bluin' o' my
  advance,
I met a derelict donkeyman who led me a merry
  dance,
Till he landed me 'n' bleached me fair in the bar
  of a rum-saloon,
'N' there he spun me a juice of a yarn to this-yer
  brand of tune.

'It's a solemn gospel, mate,' he says, 'but a man
  as ships aboard
A steamer-tramp, he gets his whack of the wonders
  of the Lord—
Such as roaches crawlin' over his bunk, 'n' snakes
  inside his bread,
And work by night and work by day enough to
  strike him dead.

'But that there's by the way,' says he ; 'the yarn
  I'm goin' to spin
Is about myself 'n' the life I led in the last ship I
  was in,
The "Esmeralda," casual tramp, from Hull towards
  the Hook,
Wi' one o' the brand o' Cain for mate 'n' a human
  mistake for cook.

'We'd a week or so of dippin' around in a wind
  from outer hell,
With a fathom or more of broken sea at large in the
  forrard well,
Till our boats were bashed and bust and broke and
  gone to Davy Jones,
'N' then come white Atlantic fog as chilled us to
  the bones.

'We slowed her down and started the horn and
  watch and watch about,
We froze the marrow in all our bones a-keepin' a
  good look-out,

'N' the ninth night out, in the middle watch, I
    woke from a pleasant dream,
With the smash of a steamer ramming our plates
    a point abaft the beam.

"'Twas cold and dark when I fetched the deck, dirty
    'n' cold 'n' thick,
'N' there was a feel in the way she rode as fairly
    turned me sick ;—
She was settlin', listin' quickly down, 'n' I heard
    the mates a-cursin',
'N' I heard the wash 'n' the grumble-grunt of a
    steamer's screws reversin'.

' She was leavin' us, mate, to sink or swim, 'n' the
    words we took 'n' said
They turned the port-light grassy-green 'n' the
    starboard rosy-red.
We give her a hot perpetual taste of the singeing
    curse of Cain,
As we heard her back 'n' clear the wreck 'n' off to
    her course again.

'Then the mate came dancin' on to the scene, 'n' he
    says, "Now quit yer chin,
Or I'll smash yer skulls, so help me James, 'n' let
    some wisdom in.
Ye dodderin' scum o' the slums," he says, "are ye
    drunk or blazin' daft?
If ye wish to save yer sickly hides, ye'd best con-
    trive a raft."

'So he spoke us fair and turned us to, 'n' we wrought
    wi' tooth and nail
Wi' scantling, casks, 'n' coops 'n' ropes, 'n' boiler-
    plates 'n' sail,
'N' all the while it were dark 'n' cold 'n' dirty as it
    could be,
'N' she was soggy 'n' settlin' down to a berth
    beneath the sea.

'Soggy she grew, 'n' she didn't lift, 'n' she listed
    more 'n' more,
Till her bell struck 'n' her boiler-pipes began to
    wheeze 'n' snore;

She settled, settled, listed, heeled, 'n' then may I
    be cust,
If her sneezin', wheezin' boiler-pipes did not begin
    to bust!

' 'N' then the stars began to shine, 'n' the birds
    began to sing,
N' the next I knowed I was bandaged up 'n' my
    arm were in a sling,
'N' a swab in uniform were there, 'n' " Well," says
    he, " 'n' how
Are yer arms, 'n' legs, 'n' liver, 'n' lungs, 'n' bones
    a-feelin' now ? "

' " Where am I ? " says I, 'n' he says, says he, a-cantin'
    to the roll,
" You 're aboard the R.M.S. ' Marie' in the after
    Glory-Hole,
'N' you 've had a shave, if you wish to know, from
    the port o' Kingdom Come.
Drink this," he says, 'n' I takes 'n' drinks, 'n' s'elp
    me, it was rum !

' Seven survivors seen 'n' saved of the "Esmeralda's"
    crowd,
Taken aboard the sweet " Marie" 'n' bunked 'n'
    treated proud,
'N' D.B.S.'d to Mersey Docks ('n' a joyful trip we
    made),
'N' there the skipper were given a purse by a
    grateful Board of Trade.

' That's the end o' the yarn,' he says, 'n' he takes
    'n' wipes his lips,
' Them's the works o' the Lord you sees in steam
    'n' sailin' ships,—
Rocks 'n' fogs 'n' shatterin' seas 'n' breakers right
    ahead,
'N' work o' nights 'n' work o' days enough to strike
    you dead.'

HELL'S PAVEMENT

'When I'm discharged in Liverpool 'n' draws my
    bit o' pay,
  I won't come to sea no more.
I'll court a pretty little lass 'n' have a weddin' day,
    'N' settle somewhere down ashore.
I'll never fare to sea again a-temptin' Davy Jones,
'A-hearkening to the cruel sharks a-hungerin' for
    my bones;
I'll run a blushin' dairy-farm or go a-crackin'
    stones,
  Or buy 'n' keep a little liquor-store,'—
                 So he said.

They towed her in to Liverpool, we made the
    hooker fast,
  And the copper-bound officials paid the crew,
And Billy drew his money, but the money didn't last,
  For he painted the alongshore blue,—

It was rum for Poll, and rum for Nan, and gin for
    Jolly Jack.
He shipped a week later in the clothes upon his
    back,
He had to pinch a little straw, he had to beg a
    sack
  To sleep on, when his watch was through,—
                 So he did.

SEA-CHANGE

' Oh Pythagoras—I sailed with thee last voyage.'
HERMAN MELVILLE.

' GONEYS an' gullies an' all o' the birds o' the sea,
   They ain't no birds, not really,' said Billy the
   Dane.
' Not mollies, nor gullies, nor goneys at all,' said
   he,
   ' But simply the sperrits of mariners livin'
   again.

' Them birds goin' fishin' is nothin' but souls o' the
   drowned,
   Souls o' the drowned an' the kicked as are never
   no more ;
An' that there haughty old albatross cruisin' around,
   Belike he 's Admiral Nelson or Admiral Noah.

' An' merry 's the life they are living.   They settle
      and dip,
   They fishes, they never stands watches, they
      waggle their wings;
When a ship comes by, they fly to look at the ship
   To see how the nowaday mariners manages
      things.

When freezing aloft in a snorter, I tell you I wish—
   (Though maybe it ain't like a Christian)—I wish
      I could be
A haughty old copper-bound albatross dipping for
      fish
   And coming the proud over all o' the birds o' the
      sea.

HARBOUR-BAR

' It was very sad about old Hal. He'd been ailing for two weeks, and died as we were towing up the river.'
AN UNOFFICIAL LOG.

ALL in the feathered palm-tree tops the bright
    green parrots screech,
The white line of the running surf goes booming
    down the beach,
But I shall never see them, though the land lies
    close aboard,
I've shaped the last long silent tack as takes one
    to the Lord.

Give me the Scripters, Jakey, 'n' my pipe atween
    my lips,
I'm bound for somewhere south and far beyond the
    track of ships ;

I've run my rags of colours up and clinched them
    to the stay,
And God the pilot's come aboard to bring me up
    the bay.

You'll mainsail-haul my bits o' things when Christ
    has took my soul,
'N' you'll lay me quiet somewhere at the landward
    end the Mole,
Where I shall hear the steamers' sterns a-squatter-
    ing from the heave,
And the topsail blocks a-piping when a rope-yarn
    fouls the sheave.

Give me a sup of lime-juice; Lord, I'm drifting
    in to port,
The landfall lies to windward and the wind comes
    light and short,
And I'm for signing off and out to take my watch
    below,
And—prop a fellow, Jakey—Lord, it's time for me
    to go!

NICIAS MORITURUS

An' Bill can have my sea-boots, Nigger Jim can
    have my knife,
    You can divvy up the dungarees an' bed,
An' the ship can have my blessing, an' the Lord can
    have my life,
    An' sails an' fish my body when I 'm dead.

An' dreaming down below there in the tangled
    greens an' blues,
    Where the sunlight shudders golden round about,
I shall hear the ships complainin' an' the cursin' of
    the crews,
    An' be sorry when the watch is tumbled out.

I shall hear them hilly-hollying the weather crojick
    brace,
    And the sucking of the wash about the hull;

When they chanty up the topsail I'll be hauling in
    my place,
  For my soul will follow seawards like a gull.

I shall hear the blocks a-grunting in the bumpkins
    over-side,
  An' the slatting of the storm-sails on the stay,
An' the rippling of the catspaw at the making of
    the tide,
  An' the swirl and splash of porpoises at play.

An' Bill can have my sea-boots, Nigger Jim can
    have my knife,
  You can divvy up the whack I haven't scofft,
An' the ship can have my blessing and the Lord
    can have my life,
  For it's time I quit the deck and went aloft.

ONE OF WALLY'S YARNS

THE watch was up on the topsail-yard a-making
    fast the sail,
'N' Joe was swiggin' his gasket taut, 'n' I felt the
    stirrup *give*,
'N' he dropped sheer from the tops'l-yard 'n' barely
    cleared the rail,
'N' o' course, we bein' aloft, *we* couldn't do nothin'—
We couldn't lower a boat and go a-lookin' for him,
For it blew hard 'n' there was sech a sea runnin'
      That no boat wouldn't live.

I seed him rise in the white o' the wake, I seed
    him lift a hand
('N' him in his oilskin suit 'n' all), I heard him lift
    a cry ;
'N' there was his place on the yard 'n' all, 'n' the
    stirrup's busted strand.

C

'N' the old man said there's a cruel old sea runnin',
A cold green Barney's Bull of a sea runnin';
It's hard, but I ain't agoin' to let a boat be lowered :
    So we left him there to die.

He couldn't have kept afloat for long an' him lashed
    up 'n' all,
'N' we couldn't see him for long, for the sea was
    blurred with the sleet 'n' snow,
'N' we couldn't think of him much because o' the
    snortin', screamin' squall.
There was a hand less at the halliards 'n' the braces,
'N' a name less when the watch spoke to the
    muster-roll,
'N' a empty bunk 'n' a pannikin as wasn't wanted
    When the watch went below.

A VALEDICTION (LIVERPOOL DOCKS)

A CRIMP.   A DRUNKEN SAILOR.

Is there anything as I can do ashore for you
When you've dropped down the tide ?—

You can take 'n' tell Nan I'm goin' about the
　　world agen,
　　　　'N' that the world's wide.
'N' tell her that there ain't no postal service
　　　　Not down on the blue sea.
'N' tell her that she'd best not keep her fires
　　alight
　　　　Nor set up late for me.
'N' tell her I'll have forgotten all about her
　　　　Afore we cross the Line.
'N' tell her that the dollars of any other sailor-
　　man
　　　　Is as good red gold as mine.

Is there anything as I can do aboard for you
Afore the tow-rope's taut ?—

I 'm new to this packet and all the ways of her,
     'N' I don't know of aught ;
But I knows as I 'm goin' down to the seas agen
     'N' the seas are salt 'n' drear ;
But I knows as all the doin' as you 're man enough
     for
        Won't make them lager-beer.

'N' ain't there nothin' as I can do ashore for you
When you 've got fair afloat ?—

You can buy a farm with the dollars as you 've done
     me of
'N' cash my advance-note.

Is there anythin' you 'd fancy for your breakfastin'
When you 're home across Mersey Bar ?—

I wants a red herrin' 'n' a prairie oyster
'N' a bucket of Three Star,

'N' a gell wi' redder lips than Polly has got,
'N' prettier ways than Nan——

*Well, so-long, Billy, 'n' a spankin' heavy pay-day to
    you !*

So-long, my fancy man !

A NIGHT AT DAGO TOM'S

On yesterday, I t'ink it was, while cruisin' down the
    street,
I met with Bill.—' Hullo,' he says, ' let's give the
    girls a treat.'
We'd red bandanas round our necks 'n' our shrouds
    new rattled down,
So we filled a couple of Santy Cruz and cleared for
    Sailor Town.

We scooted south with a press of sail till we fetched
    to a caboose,
The ' Sailor's Rest,' by Dago Tom, alongside
    ' Paddy's Goose.'
Red curtains to the windies, ay, 'n' white sand to
    the floor,
And an old blind fiddler liltin' the tune of ' Low-
    lands no more.'

He played the 'Shaking of the Sheets' 'n' the
    couples did advance,
Bowing, stamping, curtsying, in the shuffling of
    the dance ;
The old floor rocked and quivered, so it struck be-
    holders dumb,
'N' arterwards there was sweet songs 'n' good
    Jamaikey rum.

'N' there was many a merry yarn of many a merry
    spree
Aboard the ships with royals set a-sailing on the sea,
Yarns of the hooker 'Spindrift,' her as had the
    clipper-bow,—
'There ain't no ships,' says Bill to me, 'like that
    there hooker now.'

When the old blind fiddler played the tune of
    ' Pipe the Watch Below,'
The skew-eyed landlord dowsed the glim and bade
    us 'stamp 'n' go,'
'N' we linked it home, did Bill 'n' I, adown the
    scattered streets,
Until we fetched to Land o' Nod atween the linen
    sheets.

'PORT O' MANY SHIPS'

' I⊤'s a sunny pleasant anchorage, is Kingdom Come,
Where crews is always layin' aft for double-tots o'
      rum,
'N' there's dancin' 'n' fiddlin' of ev'ry kind o' sort,
It's a fine place for sailor-men is that there port.
          'N' I wish—
          I wish as I was there.

'The winds is never nothin' more than jest light
      airs,
'N' no-one gets belayin'-pinned, 'n' no-one never
      swears,
Yer free to loaf an' laze around, yer pipe atween
      yer lips,
Lollin' on the fo'c's'le, sonny, lookin' at the ships.
          'N' I wish—
          I wish as I was there.

'For ridin' in the anchorage the ships of all the
    world
Have got one anchor down 'n' all sails furled.
All the sunken hookers 'n' the crews as took 'n'
    died
They lays there merry, sonny, swingin' to the
    tide.
      'N' I wish—
      I wish as I was there.

'Drowned old wooden hookers green wi' drippin'
    wrack,
Ships as never fetched to port, as never came back,
Swingin' to the blushin' tide, dippin' to the swell,
'N' the crews all singin', sonny, beatin' on the bell.
      'N' I wish—
      I wish as I was there.'

CAPE HORN GOSPEL—I

(FOR GORDON CRAIG)

'I WAS on a hooker once,' said Karlssen,
'And Bill, as was a seaman, died,
So we lashed him in an old tarpaulin
And tumbled him across the side ;
And the fun of it was that all his gear was
Divided up among the crew
Before that blushing human error,
Our crawling little captain, knew.

'On the passage home one morning
(As certain as I prays for grace)
There was old Bill's shadder a-hauling
At the weather mizzen-topsail brace.

He was all grown green with sea-weed,
He was all lashed up and shored ;
So I says to him, I says, " Why, Billy !
What 's a-bringin' of you back aboard ? "

' " I 'm a-weary of them there mermaids,"
Says old Bill's ghost to me ;
" It ain't no place for a Christian
Below there—under sea.
For it 's all blown sand and shipwrecks,
And old bones eaten bare,
And them cold fishy females
With long green weeds for hair.

' " And there ain't no dances shuffled,
And no old yarns is spun,
And there ain't no stars but starfish,
And never any moon or sun.
I heard your keel a-passing
And the running rattle of the brace,"
And he says " Stand by," says William,
" For a shift towards a better place."

'Well, he sogered about decks till sunrise,
When a rooster in the hen-coop crowed,
And as so much smoke he faded
And as so much smoke he goed ;
And I've often wondered since, Jan,
How his old ghost stands to fare
Long o' them cold fishy females
With long green weeds for hair.'

CAPE HORN GOSPEL—II

Jake was a dirty Dago lad, an' he gave the skipper
    chin,
An' the skipper up an' took him a crack with an
    iron belaying-pin
Which stiffened him out a rusty corp, as pretty as
    you could wish,
An' then we shovelled him up in a sack an'
    dumped him to the fish.
       That was jest arter we 'd got sail on her.

Josey slipped from the tops'l-yard an' bust his
    bloody back
(Which comed from playing the giddy goat an'
    leavin' go the jack);
We lashed his chips in clouts of sail an' ballasted
    him with stones,
'The Lord hath taken away,' we says, an' we give
    him to Davy Jones.
       An' that was afore we were up with the Line.

Joe were chippin' a rusty plate a-squattin' upon
    the deck,
An' all the watch he had the sun a-singein' him on
    the neck,
An' forrard he falls at last, he does, an' he lets his
    mallet go,
Dead as a nail with a calenture, an' that was the
    end of Joe.
        An' that was just afore we made the Plate.

All o' the rest were sailor-men, an' it come to rain
    an' squall,
An' then it was halliards, sheets, an' tacks 'clue
    up, an' let go all.'
We snugged her down an' hove her to, an' the old
    contrairy cuss
Started a plate, an' settled an' sank, an' that was
    the end of us.

We slopped around on coops an' planks in the cold
    an' in the dark,
An' Bill were drowned, an' Tom were ate by a
    swine of a cruel shark,

An' a mail-boat reskied Harry an' I (which comed
    of pious prayers),
Which brings me here a-kickin' my heels in the
    port of Buenos Ayres.

I 'm bound for home in the 'Oronook,' in a suit of
    looted duds,
A D.B.S. a-earnin' a stake by helpin' peelin' spuds,
An' if ever I fetch to Prince's Stage an' sets my
    feet ashore,
You bet your hide that there I stay, an' follers the
    sea no more.

MOTHER CAREY

(AS TOLD ME BY THE BO'SUN)

MOTHER CAREY? She's the mother o' the witches
   'N' all *them* sort o' rips;
She's a fine gell to look at, but the hitch is,
   She's a sight too fond of ships.
She lives upon a iceberg to the norred,
   An' her man he's Davy Jones,
'N' she combs the weeds upon her forred
   With pore drowned sailors' bones.

She's the mother o' the wrecks, 'n' the mother
   Of all big winds as blows;
She's up to some deviltry or other
   When it storms, or sleets, or snows.
The noise of the wind's her screamin',
   'I'm arter a plump, young, fine,
Brass-buttoned, beefy-ribbed young seam'n
   So as me 'n' my mate kin dine.'

She's a hungry old rip 'n' a cruel
  For sailor-men like we,
She's give a many mariners the gruel
  'N' a long sleep under sea.
She's the blood o' many a crew upon her
  'N' the bones of many a wreck,
'N' she's barnacles a-growin' on her
  'N' shark's teeth round her neck.

I ain't never had no schoolin'
  Nor read no books like you,
But I knows 't ain't healthy to be foolin'
  With that there gristly two.
You're young, you thinks, 'n' you're lairy,
  But if you're to make old bones,
Steer clear, I says, o' Mother Carey
  'N' that there Davy Jones.

EVENING—REGATTA DAY

YOUR nose is a red jelly, your mouth's a toothless
    wreck,
And I'm atop of you, banging your head upon the
    dirty deck ;
And both your eyes are bunged and blind like
    those of a mewling pup,
For you're the juggins who caught the crab and
    lost the ship the Cup.

He caught a crab in the spurt home, this blushing
    cherub did,
And the 'Craigie's' whaler slipped ahead like a
    cart-wheel on the skid,
And beat us fair by a boat's nose though we
    sweated fit to start her,
So we are playing at Nero now, and *he's* the
    Christian martyr.

And Stroke is lashing a bunch of keys to the
    buckle-end a belt,
And we 're going to lay you over a chest and baste
    you till you melt.
The 'Craigie' boys are beating the bell and
    cheering down the tier,
D' ye hear, you Port Mahone baboon, I ask you, do
    you *hear*?

A VALEDICTION

We're bound for blue water where the great winds
    blow,
It's time to get the tacks aboard, time for us to
    go;
The crowd's at the capstan and the tune's in the
    shout,
' A long pull, a strong pull, *and warp the hooker out.*'

The bow-wash is eddying, spreading from the bows,
Aloft and loose the topsails and some one give a
    rouse;
A salt Atlantic chanty shall be music to the dead,
' A long pull, a strong pull, *and the yard to the mast-
    head.*'

Green and merry run the seas, the wind comes
    cold,
Salt and strong and pleasant, and worth a mint o'
    gold;

And she's staggering, swooping, as she feels her
 feet,
'A long pull, a strong pull, *and aft the main-sheet.*'

Shrilly squeal the running sheaves, the weather-
 gear strains,
Such a clatter o' chain-sheets, the devil's in the
 chains ;
Over us the bright stars, under us the drowned,
'A long pull, a strong pull, *and we're outward
 bound.*'

Yonder, round and ruddy, is the mellow old moon,
The red-funnelled tug has gone, and now, sonny,
 soon
We'll be clear of the Channel, so watch how you
 steer,
'Ease her when she pitches, *and so-long, my dear.*'

A PIER-HEAD CHORUS

Oh I'll be chewing salted horse and biting flinty
    bread,
And dancing, with the stars to watch, upon the
    fo'c's'le head,
Hearkening to the bow-wash and the welter of the
    tread
  Of a thousand tons of clipper running free.

For the tug has got the tow-rope and will take us
    to the Downs,
Her paddles churn the river-wrack to muddy greens
    and browns,
And I have given river-wrack and all the filth of
    towns
  For the rolling, combing cresters of the sea.

We'll sheet the mizzen-royals home and shimmer
    down the Bay,

The sea-line blue with billows, the land-line blurred
    and grey;
The bow-wash will be piling high and thrashing
    into spray,
  As the hooker's fore-foot tramples down the
    swell.

She'll log a giddy seventeen and rattle out the
    reel,
The weight of all the run-out line will be a thing
    to feel,
As the bacca-quidding shell-back shambles aft to
    take the wheel,
  And the sea-sick little middy strikes the bell.

THE GOLDEN CITY OF ST. MARY

(for f. c. h.)

Out beyond the sunset, could I but find the way,
Is a sleepy blue laguna which widens to a bay,
And there's the Blessed City—so the sailors say—
　　The Golden City of St. Mary.

It's built of fair marble—white—without a stain,
And in the cool twilight when the sea-winds wane
The bells chime faintly, like a soft, warm rain,
　　In the Golden City of St. Mary.

Among the green palm-trees where the fire-flies
　　shine,
Are the white tavern tables where the gallants
　　dine,
Singing slow Spanish songs like old mulled wine,
　　In the Golden City of St. Mary.

Oh I 'll be shipping sunset-wards and westward-ho
Through the green toppling combers a-shattering
    into snow,
Till I come to quiet moorings and a watch below,
    In the Golden City of St. Mary.

TRADE WINDS

In the harbour, in the island, in the Spanish Seas,
Are the tiny white houses and the orange-trees,
And day-long, night-long, the cool and pleasant
    breeze
  Of the steady Trade Winds blowing.

There is the red wine, the nutty Spanish ale,
The shuffle of the dancers, the old salt's tale,
The squeaking fiddle, and the soughing in the sail
  Of the steady Trade Winds blowing.

And o' nights there's fire-flies and the yellow moon,
And in the ghostly palm-trees the sleepy tune
Of the quiet voice calling me, the long low croon
  Of the steady Trade Winds blowing.

SEA-FEVER

I MUST down to the seas again, to the lonely sea
 and the sky,
And all I ask is a tall ship and a star to steer her
 by,
And the wheel's kick and the wind's song and the
 white sail's shaking,
And a grey mist on the sea's face and a grey dawn
 breaking.

I must down to the seas again, for the call of the
 running tide
Is a wild call and a clear call that may not be
 denied ;
And all I ask is a windy day with the white clouds
 flying,
And the flung spray and the blown spume, and the
 sea-gulls crying.

I must down to the seas again to the vagrant gypsy
    life,
To the gull's way and the whale's way where the
    wind's like a whetted knife;
And all I ask is a merry yarn from a laughing
    fellow-rover,
And quiet sleep and a sweet dream when the long
    trick's over.

A WANDERER'S SONG

(FOR W. B. YEATS)

A WIND's in the heart o' me, a fire's in my heels,
I am tired of brick and stone and rumbling wagon-
 wheels;
I hunger for the sea's edge, the limits of the land,
Where the wild old Atlantic is shouting on the
 sand.

Oh I'll be going, leaving the noises of the street,
To where a lifting foresail-foot is yanking at the
 sheet;
To a windy, tossing anchorage where yawls and
 ketches ride,
Oh I'll be going, going, until I meet the tide.

And first I'll hear the sea-wind, the mewing of the
 gulls,
The clucking, sucking of the sea about the rusty
 hulls,

The songs at the capstan in the hooker warping
    out,
And then the heart of me 'll know I 'm there or
    thereabout.

Oh I am tired of brick and stone, the heart o' me
    is sick,
For windy green, unquiet sea, the realm o' Moby
    Dick ;
And I 'll be going, going, from the roaring of the
    wheels,
For a wind 's in the heart o' me, a fire 's in my
    heels,

CARDIGAN BAY

(FOR LAURENCE BINYON)

CLEAN, green, windy billows notching out the sky,
Grey clouds tattered into rags, sea-winds blowing
    high,
And the ships under topsails, beating, thrashing by,
   And the mewing of the herring gulls.

Dancing, flashing green seas shaking white locks,
Boiling in blind eddies over hidden rocks,
And the wind in the rigging, the creaking o' the
    blocks,
   And the straining of the timber hulls.

Delicate, cool sea-weeds, green and amber-brown,
In beds where shaken sunlight slowly filters down
On many a drowned seventy-four, many a sunken
    town,
   And the whitening of the dead men's skulls.

CHRISTMAS EVE AT SEA

(FOR F. C. H.)

A WIND is rustling 'south and soft,'
  Cooing a quiet country tune,
The calm sea sighs, and far aloft
  The sails are ghostly in the moon.

Unquiet ripples lisp and purr,
  A block there pipes and chirps i' the sheave,
The wheel-ropes jar, the reef-points stir
  Faintly—and it is Christmas Eve.

The hushed sea seems to hold her breath,
  And o'er the giddy, swaying spars,
Silent and excellent as Death,
  The dim blue skies are bright with stars.

Dear God—they shone in Palestine
  Like this, and yon pale moon serene
Looked down among the lowing kine
  On Mary and the Nazarene.

The angels called from deep to deep,
  The burning heavens felt the thrill,
Startling the flocks of silly sheep
  And lonely shepherds on the hill.

To-night beneath the dripping bows
  Where flashing bubbles burst and throng,
The bow-wash murmurs and sighs and soughs
  A message from the angels' song.

The moon goes nodding down the west,
  The drowsy helmsman strikes the bell;
Rex Judæorum natus est,
  I charge you, brothers, sing *Nowell,*
  Nowell,
Rex Judæorum natus est.

E

A BALLAD OF CAPE ST. VINCENT

Now, Bill, ain't it prime to be a-sailin',
    Slippin' easy, splashin' up the sea,
Dossin' snug aneath the weather-railin',
    Quiddin' bonded Jacky out a-lee ?
English sea astern us and afore us,
    Reaching out three thousand miles ahead,
God's own stars a-risin' solemn o'er us,
        And — yonder's Cape St. Vincent and the
        Dead.

There they lie, Bill, man and mate together,
    Dreamin' out the dog-watch down below,
Anchored in the port of Pleasant Weather,
    Waiting for the Bo'sun's call to blow.
Over them the tide goes lappin', swayin',
    Under them's the wide bay's muddy bed,
And it's pleasant dreams—to them—to hear us
        sayin',
        Yonder's Cape St. Vincent and the Dead.

Hear that P. and O. boat's engines dronin',
    Beating out of time and out of tune,
Ripping past with every plate a-groanin',
    Spitting smoke and cinders at the moon?
Ports a-lit like little stars a-settin',
    See 'em glintin' yaller, green, and red,
Loggin' twenty knots, Bill,—but forgettin',
    Yonder's Cape St. Vincent and the Dead.

They're 'discharged' now, Billy, 'left the
    service,'
Rough an' bitter was the watch they stood,
Drake an' Blake, an' Collingwood an' Jervis,
    Nelson, Rodney, Hawke, an' Howe an' Hood.
They'd a hard time, haulin' an' directin',
    There's the flag they left us, Billy—tread
Straight an' keep it flyin'—recollectin',
    Yonder's Cape St. Vincent and the Dead.

THE TARRY BUCCANEER

(FOR JACK B. YEATS)

AIR : *The Fine Old English Gentleman*

I 'M going to be a pirate with a bright brass pivot-
gun,
And an island in the Spanish Main beyond the
setting sun,
And a silver flagon full of red wine to drink when
work is done,
Like a fine old salt-sea scavenger, like a tarry
Buccaneer.

With a sandy creek to careen in, and a pig-tailed
Spanish mate,
And under my main-hatches a sparkling merry
freight

Of doubloons and double moidores and pieces of
 eight,
 Like a fine old salt-sea scavenger, like a tarry
  Buccaneer.

With a taste for Spanish wine-shops and for spend-
 ing my doubloons,
And a crew of swart mulattoes and black-eyed
 octoroons,
And a thoughtful way with mutineers of making
 them maroons,
 Like a fine old salt-sea scavenger, like a tarry
  Buccaneer.

With a sash of crimson velvet and a diamond-hilted
 sword,
And a silver whistle about my neck secured to a
 golden cord,
And a habit of taking captives and walking them
 along a board,
 Like a fine old salt-sea scavenger, like a tarry
  Buccaneer.

With a spy-glass tucked beneath my arm and a
    cocked hat cocked askew,
And a long low rakish schooner a-cutting of the
    waves in two,
And a flag of skull and cross-bones the wickedest
    that ever flew,
  Like a fine old salt-sea scavenger, like a tarry
  Buccaneer.

A BALLAD OF JOHN SILVER

WE were schooner-rigged and rakish, with a long
and lissome hull,
And we flew the pretty colours of the cross-bones
and the skull;
We'd a big black Jolly Roger flapping grimly at
the fore,
And we sailed the Spanish Water in the happy days
of yore.

We'd a long brass gun amidships, like a well-
conducted ship,
We had each a brace of pistols and a cutlass at the
hip;
It's a point which tells against us, and a fact to be
deplored,
But we chased the goodly merchant-men and laid
their ships aboard.

Then the dead men fouled the scuppers and the
wounded filled the chains,
And the paint-work all was spatter-dashed with
other people's brains,
She was boarded, she was looted, she was scuttled
till she sank,
And the pale survivors left us by the medium of
the plank.

O! then it was (while standing by the taffrail on
the poop)
We could hear the drowning folk lament the absent
chicken-coop;
Then, having washed the blood away, we'd little
else to do
Than to dance a quiet hornpipe as the old salts
taught us to.

O! the fiddle on the fo'c's'le, and the slapping
naked soles,
And the genial 'Down the middle, Jake, and
curtsy when she rolls!'

With the silver seas around us and the pale moon
    overhead,
And the look-out not a-looking and his pipe-bowl
    glowing red.

Ah ! the pig-tailed, quidding pirates and the pretty
    pranks we played,
All have since been put a stop-to by the naughty
    Board of Trade ;
The schooners and the merry crews are laid away
    to rest,
A little south the sunset in the Islands of the
    Blest.

LYRICS FROM 'THE BUCCANEER'

I

WE are far from sight of the harbour lights,
  Of the sea-ports whence we came,
But the old sea calls and the cold wind bites,
  And our hearts are turned to flame.

And merry and rich is the goodly gear
  We 'll win upon the tossing sea,
A silken gown for my dainty dear,
  And a gold doubloon for me.

It 's the old old road and the old old quest
  Of the cut-throat sons of Cain,
South by west and a quarter west,
  And hey for the Spanish Main.

II

There's a sea-way somewhere where all day long
   Is the hushed susurrus of the sea,
The mewing of the skuas, and the sailor's song,
   And the wind's cry calling me.

There's a haven somewhere where the quiet o' the
     bay
   Is troubled with the shifting tide,
Where the gulls are flying, crying in the bright
     white spray,
   And the tan-sailed schooners ride.

III

THE toppling rollers at the harbour mouth
    Are spattering the bows with foam,
And the anchor's catted, and she's heading for the
        south
    With her topsails sheeted home.

And a merry measure is the dance she'll tread
    (To the clanking of the staysail's hanks)
When the guns are growling and the blood runs
        red,
    And the prisoners are walking o' the planks.

D'AVALOS' PRAYER

WHEN the last sea is sailed and the last shallow
    charted,
  When the last field is reaped and the last harvest
    stored,
When the last fire is out and the last guest departed,
  Grant the last prayer that I shall pray, Be good
    to me, O Lord!

And let me pass in a night at sea, a night of storm
    and thunder,
  In the loud crying of the wind through sail and
    rope and spar ;
Send me a ninth great peaceful wave to drown and
    roll me under
  To the cold tunny-fishes' home where the drowned
    galleons are.

And in the dim green quiet place far out of sight
  and hearing,
    Grant I may hear at whiles the wash and thresh
    of the sea-foam
About the fine keen bows of the stately clippers
  steering
    Towards the lone northern star and the fair ports
    of home.

THE WEST WIND

IT'S a warm wind, the west wind, full of birds'
    cries;
I never hear the west wind but tears are in my
    eyes.
For it comes from the west lands, the old brown
    hills,
And April's in the west wind, and daffodils.

It's a fine land, the west land, for hearts as tired as
    mine,
Apple orchards blossom there, and the air's like
    wine.
There is cool green grass there, where men may lie
    at rest,
And the thrushes are in song there, fluting from the
    nest.

'Will ye not come home, brother? ye have been
    long away,
It 's April, and blossom time, and white is the may;
And bright is the sun, brother, and warm is the
    rain,—
Will ye not come home, brother, home to us again?

'The young corn is green, brother, where the
    rabbits run,
It 's blue sky, and white clouds, and warm rain and
    sun.
It 's song to a man's soul, brother, fire to a man's
    brain,
To hear the wild bees and see the merry spring
    again.

'Larks are singing in the west, brother, above the
    green wheat,
So will ye not come home, brother, and rest your
    tired feet?
I 've a balm for bruised hearts, brother, sleep for
    aching eyes,'
Says the warm wind, the west wind, full of birds'
    cries.

It's the white road westwards is the road I must
  tread
To the green grass, the cool grass, and rest for
  heart and head,
To the violets and the warm hearts and the thrushes'
  song,
In the fine land, the west land, the land where I
  belong.

THE GALLEY-ROWERS

STAGGERING over the running combers
   The long-ship heaves her dripping flanks,
Singing together, the sea-roamers
   Drive the oars grunting in the banks.
      A long pull,
      And a long long pull to Mydath.

'Where are ye bound, ye swart sea-farers,
   Vexing the grey wind-angered brine,
Bearers of home-spun cloth, and bearers
   Of goat-skins filled with country wine?'

'We are bound sunset-wards, not knowing,
   Over the whale's way miles and miles,
Going to Vine-Land, haply going
   To the Bright Beach of the Blessed Isles.

' In the wind's teeth and the spray's stinging
   Westward and outward forth we go,
Knowing not whither nor why, but singing
   An old old oar-song as we row.
       A long pull,
       And a long long pull to Mydath.'

SORROW O' MYDATH

WEARY the cry of the wind is, weary the sea,
Weary the heart and the mind and the body o' me.
Would I were out of it, done with it, would I
    could be
    A white gull crying along the desolate sands!

Outcast, derelict soul in a body accurst,
Standing drenched with the spindrift, standing
    athirst,
For the cool green waves of death to arise and
    burst
    In a tide of quiet for me on the desolate sands.

Would that the waves and the long white hair o' the
    spray
Would gather in splendid terror and blot me away
To the sunless place o' the wrecks where the waters
    sway
    Gently, dreamily, quietly over desolate sands!

VAGABOND

Dunno a heap about the what an' why,
    Can't say 's I ever knowed.
Heaven to me 's a fair blue stretch of sky,
    Earth 's jest a dusty road.

Dunno the names o' things, nor what they are,
    Can't say 's I ever will.
Dunno about God—He 's jest the noddin' star
    Atop the windy hill.

Dunno about Life—it 's jest a tramp alone
    From wakin'-time to doss.
Dunno about Death—it 's jest a quiet stone
    All over-grey wi' moss.

An' why I live, an' why the old world spins,
    Are things I never knowed ;
My mark 's the gypsy fires, the lonely inns,
    An' jest the dusty road.

VISION

I HAVE drunken the red wine and flung the dice ;
   Yet once in the noisy ale-house I have seen and
     heard
The dear pale lady with the mournful eyes,
   And a voice like that of a pure grey cooing
     bird.

With delicate white hands—white hands that I
     have kist
   (Oh frail white hands !)—she soothed my aching
     eyes ;
And her hair fell about her in a dim clinging
     mist,
   Like smoke from a golden incense burned in
     Paradise.

With gentle loving words, like shredded balm and
    myrrh,
  She healed with sweet forgiveness my black
    bitter sins,
Then passed into the night, and I go seeking her
  Down the dark, silent streets, past the warm,
    lighted inns.

SPUNYARN

Spunyarn, spunyarn, with one to turn the crank,
And one to slather the spunyarn, and one to knot
    the hank ;
It's an easy job for a summer watch, and a pleasant
    job enough,
To twist the tarry lengths of yarn to shapely sailor
    stuff.

Life is nothing but spunyarn on a winch in need of
    oil,
Little enough is twined and spun but fever-fret
    and moil.
I have travelled on land and sea, and all that I
    have found
Are these poor songs to brace the arms that help
    the winches round.

THE DEAD KNIGHT

THE cleanly rush of the mountain air,
And the mumbling, grumbling humble-bees,
Are the only things that wander there.
The pitiful bones are laid at ease,
The grass has grown in his tangled hair,
And a rambling bramble binds his knees.

To shrieve his soul from the pangs of hell,
The only requiem-bells that rang
Were the hare-bell and the heather-bell.
Hushed he is with the holy spell
In the gentle hymn the wind sang,
And he lies quiet, and sleeps well.

He is bleached and blanched with the summer
        sun ;
The misty rain and the cold dew

Have altered him from the kingly one
(That his lady loved, and his men knew)
And dwindled him to a skeleton.

The vetches have twined about his bones,
The straggling ivy twists and creeps
In his eye-sockets; the nettle keeps
Vigil about him while he sleeps.
Over his body the wind moans
With a dreary tune throughout the day,
In a chorus wistful, eerie, thin
As the gull's cry—as the cry in the bay,
The mournful word the seas say
When tides are wandering out or in.

PERSONAL

TRAMPING at night in the cold and wet, I passed
    the lighted inn,
And an old tune, a sweet tune, was being played
    within.
It was full of the laugh of the leaves and the song
    the wind sings;
It brought the tears and the choked throat, and a
    catch to the heart-strings.

And it brought a bitter thought of the days that
    now were dead to me,
The merry days in the old home before I went to
    sea—
Days that were dead to me indeed. I bowed my
    head to the rain,
And I passed by the lighted inn to the lonely roads
    again.

ON MALVERN HILL

A WIND is brushing down the clover,
    It sweeps the tossing branches bare,
Blowing the poising kestrel over
    The crumbling ramparts of the Caer.

It whirls the scattered leaves before us
    Along the dusty road to home,
Once it awakened into chorus
    The heart-strings in the ranks of Rome.

There by the gusty coppice border
    The shrilling trumpets broke the halt,
The Roman line, the Roman order,
    Swayed forwards to the blind assault.

Spearman and charioteer and bowman
    Charged and were scattered into spray,
Savage and taciturn the Roman
    Hewed upwards in the Roman way.

There—in the twilight—where the cattle
  Are lowing home across the fields,
The beaten warriors left the battle
  Dead on the clansmen's wicker shields.

The leaves whirl in the wind's riot
  Beneath the Beacon's jutting spur,
Quiet are clan and chief, and quiet
  Centurion and signifer.

TEWKESBURY ROAD

It is good to be out on the road, and going one
    knows not where,
  Going through meadow and village, one knows
    not whither nor why;
Through the grey light drift o' the dust, in the
    keen cool rush o' the air,
  Under the flying white clouds, and the broad
    blue lift o' the sky;

And to halt at the chattering brook, in the tall
    green fern at the brink
  Where the harebell grows, and the gorse, and
    the fox-gloves purple and white;
Where the shy-eyed delicate deer troop down to
    the pools to drink,
  When the stars are mellow and large at the
    coming on of the night.

O ! to feel the warmth o' the rain, and the homely
smell o' the earth,
Is a tune for the blood to jig to, a joy past
power of words;
And the blessed green comely meadows seem all
a-ripple with mirth
At the lilt of the shifting feet, and the dear
wild cry o' the birds.

ON EASTNOR KNOLL

Silent are the woods, and the dim green boughs are
Hushed in the twilight : yonder, in the path through
The apple orchard, is a tired plough-boy
Calling the kine home.

A bright white star blinks, the pale moon rounds, but
Still the red, lurid wreckage of the sunset
Smoulders in smoky fire, and burns on
The misty hill-tops.

Ghostly it grows, and darker, the burning
Fades into smoke, and now the gusty oaks are
A silent army of phantoms thronging
A land of shadows.

'REST HER SOUL, SHE'S DEAD!'

She has done with the sea's sorrow and the
    world's way
  And the wind's grief;
Strew her with laurel, cover her with bay
  And ivy-leaf.
Let the slow mournful music sound before her,
Strew the white flowers about the bier, and
    o'er her
  The sleepy poppies red beyond belief.

On the black velvet covering her eyes
  Let the dull earth be thrown;
Hers is the mightier silence of the skies,
  And long, quiet rest alone.
Over the pure, dark, wistful eyes of her,
O'er all the human, all that dies of her,
  Gently let flowers be strown.

G

Lay her away in quiet old peaceful earth
  (This blossom of ours),
She has done with the world's anger and the
    world's mirth,
  Sunshine and rain-showers;
And over the poor, sad, tired face of her,
In the long grass above the place of her
(The grass which hides the glory and the grace
    of her),
  May the Spring bring the flowers.

'ALL YE THAT PASS BY'

On the long dusty ribbon of the long city street,
The pageant of life is passing me on multitudinous
feet,
With a word here of the hills, and a song there of
the sea,
And—the great movement changes—the pageant
passes me.

Faces—passionate faces—of men I may not know,
They haunt me, burn me to the heart, as I turn
aside to go :
The king's face and the cur's face, and the face of
the stuffed swine,
They are passing, they are passing, their eyes look
into mine.

I never can tire of the music of the noise of many
    feet,
The thrill of the blood pulsing, the tick of the
    heart's beat,
Of the men many as sands, of the squadrons ranked
    and massed
Who are passing, changing always, and never have
    changed or passed.

IN MEMORY OF A. P. R.

ONCE in the windy wintry weather,
  The road dust blowing in our eyes,
We starved and tramped or slept together
  Beneath the haystacks and the skies ;

Until the tiring tramp was over,
  And then the wind for him was blown,
He left his friend—his fellow-rover—
  To tramp the dusty roads alone.

The winds wail and the woods are yellow,
  The hills are blotted in the rain,
'And would he were with me,' sighs his fellow,
  'With me upon the roads again !'

TO-MORROW

Oh yesterday the cutting edge drank thirstily and
    deep,
The upland outlaws ringed us in and herded us as
    sheep,
They drove us from the stricken field and bayed us
    into keep;
        But to-morrow,
  By the living God, we'll try the game again!

Oh yesterday our little troop was ridden through
    and through,
Our swaying, tattered pennons fled, a broken, beaten
    few,
And all a summer afternoon they hunted us and
    slew;
        But to-morrow,
  By the living God, we'll try the game again!

And here upon the turret-top the bale-fire glowers
    red,
The wake-lights burn and drip about our hacked,
    disfigured dead,
And many a broken heart is here and many a
    broken head ;
        But to-morrow,
By the living God, we 'll try the game again !

CAVALIER

ALL the merry kettle-drums are thudding into
    rhyme,
    Dust is swimming dizzily down the village street,
The scabbards are clattering, the feathers nodding
    time,
    To a clink of many horses' shoes, a tramp of many
    feet.

Seven score of Cavaliers fighting for the King,
    Trolling lusty stirrup-songs, clamouring for wine,
Riding with a loose rein, marching with a swing,
    Beneath the blue bannerol of Rupert of the
    Rhine.

Hey the merry company !—the loud fifes playing—
    Blue scarves and bright steel and blossom of the
    may,

Roses in the feathered hats, the long plumes
   swaying,
A king's son ahead of them showing them the
   way.

A SONG AT PARTING

THE tick of the blood is settling slow, my heart will
    soon be still,
And ripe and ready am I for rest in the grave atop
    the hill ;
So gather me up and lay me down, for ready and
    ripe am I,
For the weary vigil with sightless eyes that may
    not see the sky.

I have lived my life : I have spilt the wine that
    God the Maker gave,
So carry me up the lonely hill and lay me in the
    grave,
And cover me in with cleanly mould and old and
    lichened stones,
In a place where ever the cry of the wind shall
    thrill my sleepy bones.

Gather me up and lay me down with an old song
    and a prayer,
Cover me in with wholesome earth, and weep and
    leave me there ;
And get you gone with a kindly thought and an
    old tune and a sigh,
And leave me alone, asleep, at rest, for ready and
    ripe am I.

GLOSSARY

Abaft the beam.—That half of a ship included between her amid-ship section and the taffrail. (For ' taffrail,' *see* below.)

Abel Brown.—An unquotable sea-song.

Advance-note.—A note for one month's wages issued to sailors on their signing a ship's articles.

Belaying-pins.—Bars of iron or hard wood to which running rigging may be secured or *belayed.*

Belaying-pins, from their handiness and peculiar club-shape, are sometimes used as bludgeons.

Bloody.—An intensive derived from the substantive 'blood,' a name applied to the Bucks, Scowrers, and Mohocks of the seventeenth and eighteenth centuries.

Blue Peter.—A blue and white flag hoisted at the foretrucks of ships about to sail.

Bollard.—From *bōl* or *bole*, the round trunk of a tree. A phallic or 'sparklet'-shaped ornament of the dockside, of assistance to mariners in warping into or out of dock.

Bonded Jacky.—Negro-head tobacco or sweet cake.

Bull of Barney.—A beast mentioned in an unquotable sea-proverb.

Bumpkin.—An iron bar (projecting out-board from the ship's side) to which the lower and topsail brace blocks are some-times hooked.

Cape Horn fever.—The illness proper to malingerers.

Catted.—Said of an anchor when weighed and secured to the 'cat-head.'

Chanty.—A song sung to lighten labour at the capstan, sheets, and halliards. The soloist is known as the chantyman, and is usually a person of some authority in the fo'c's'le. Many chanties are of great beauty and extreme antiquity.

Clipper-bow.—A bow of delicate curves and lines.

Clout.—A rag or cloth. Also a blow:—'I fetched him a clout i' the lug.'

Crimp.—A sort of scoundrelly land-shark preying upon sailors.

D.B.S.—Distressed British Sailor. A term applied to those who are invalided home from foreign ports.

Dungaree.—A cheap, rough thin cloth (generally blue or brown), woven, I am told, of cocoa-nut fibre.

Forward or *Forrard.*—Towards the bows.

Fo'c's'le (Forecastle).—The deck-house or living-room of the crew. The word is often used to indicate the crew, or those members of it described by passengers as the 'common sailors.'

Fore-stay.—A powerful wire rope supporting the foremast forward.

Gaskets.—Ropes or plaited lines used to secure the sails in furling.

Goneys.—Albatrosses.

Guffy.—A marine or jolly.

Gullies.—Sea-gulls, Cape Horn pigeons, etc.

Heave and pawl.—A cry of encouragement at the capstan.

Hooker.—A periphrasis for ship, I suppose from a ship's carrying *hooks* or anchors.

Jack or *Jackstay.*—A slender iron rail running along the upper portions of the yards in some ships.

Leeward.—Pronounced 'looard.' That quarter to which the wind blows.

Mainsail haul.—An order in tacking ship bidding 'swing the mainyards.' To loot, steal, or 'acquire.'

Main-shrouds.—Ropes, usually wire, supporting lateral strains upon the mainmast.

Mollies.—Molly-hawks, or Fulmar petrels. Wide-winged dusky sea-fowls, common in high latitudes, oily to taste, gluttonous. Great fishers and garbage-eaters.

Port Mahon Baboon, or *Port Mahon Soger.*—I have been unable to discover either the origin of these insulting epithets or the reasons for the peculiar bitterness with which they sting the marine recipient. They are older than Dana (*circa* 1840).

An old merchant sailor, now dead, once told me that Port Mahon was that godless city from which the Ark set sail, in which case the name may have some traditional connection with that evil 'Mahoun' or 'Mahu,' prince of darkness, mentioned by Shakespeare and some of our older poets.

The real Port Mahon, a fine harbour in Minorca, was taken by the French, from Admiral Byng, in the year 1756.

I think that the phrases originated at the time of Byng's consequent trial and execution.

Purchase.—*See* 'Tackle.'

Quidding.—Tobacco-chewing.

Sails.—The sail-maker.
Santa Cruz.—A brand of rum.
Scantling.—Planks.
Soger.—A laggard, malingerer, or hang-back. To loaf or skulk or work Tom Cox's Traverse.
Spunyarn.—A three-strand line spun out of old rope-yarns knotted together. Most sailing-ships carry a spunyarn winch, and the spinning of such yarn is a favourite occupation in fine weather.
Stirrup.—A short rope supporting the foot-rope on which the sailors stand when aloft on the yards.

Tack.—To stay or 'bout ship. A reach to windward. The weather lower corner of a course.
Tackle.—Pronounced *taykle.* A combination of pulleys for the obtaining of artificial power.

Taffrail.—The rail or bulwark round the sternmost end of a ship's poop or after-deck.

Trick.—The ordinary two-hour spell at the wheel or on the look-out.

Windward or *Weather.*—That quarter from which the wind blows.

Edinburgh : Printed by T. and A. Constable

FURTHER READING

Biographical/Autobiographical

Masefield, John, *So Long to Learn*, London: Heinemann, 1952

Babington Smith, Constance, *John Masefield – A Life*, Oxford: Oxford University Press, 1978

Critical

Binding, Paul, *An Endless Quiet Valley – A Reappraisal of John Masefield*, Woonton Almeley, Herefordshire: Logaston Press, 1998

Dwyer, June, *John Masefield*, New York: Ungar, 1987

Spark, Muriel, *John Masefield*, London: Hutchinson, revised edition, 1991

Sternlicht, Sanford, *John Masefield*, Boston, Mass: Twayne Publishers, 1977

Strong, L.A.G., *John Masefield*, London: Longmans, Green and Co., corrected edition, 1964

Bibliographical

Simmons, Charles H., *A Bibliography of John Masefield*, New York: Columbia University Press, 1930

Handley-Taylor, Geoffrey, *John Masefield, O.M. The Queen's Poet Laureate. A Bibliography and Eighty-First Birthday Tribute,* London: Cranbrook Tower Press, 1960

Wight, Crocker, *John Masefield - A Bibliographical Description of his First, Limited, Signed and Special Editions*, Boston, Mass: Library of the Boston Athenaeum, second edition, 1992

Errington, Philip W., *John Masefield - The Great Auk of English Literature, A Bibliography*, New Castle, DE: Oak Knoll Press [forthcoming, 2003]

Poetry

Masefield, John, *Collected Poems*, London: Heinemann, 1923; Heinemann, [second] edition, 1932; Heinemann, [third] edition, 1938

Masefield, John, *Poems*, London: Heinemann, 1946

Children's

Masefield, John, *The Midnight Folk*, London: Heinemann, 1927 (and subsequent reprints)

Masefield, John, *The Box of Delights*, London: Heinemann, 1935 (and subsequent reprints)

Novels

Masefield, John, *Sard Harker*, London: Heinemann, 1924

Masefield, John, *ODTAA*, London: Heinemann, 1926

Masefield, John, *Dead Ned*, London: Heinemann, 1938

Published Collections of Letters

Buchan, William (ed.), *Letters to Reyna*, London: Buchan and Enright, 1983

Lamont, Corliss and Lansing Lamont (eds), *Letters of John Masefield to Florence Lamont,* New York: Columbia University Press, 1979

Vansittart, Peter (ed.), *John Masefield's Letters from the Front 1915-1917*, London: Constable, 1984

The John Masefield Society was formed in 1992 to stimulate the appreciation of, and interest in, the life and works of John Masefield. The Society is based in Ledbury, the Herefordshire market town of his birth, and holds various public events in addition to publishing a journal and occasional papers.

For more details please contact:
The John Masefield Society
'The Frith', Ledbury, Herefordshire. HR8 1LW.
United Kingdom.